SLYTHERIN.

RAVENCLAW.

GRYFFINDOR™

SEEKER

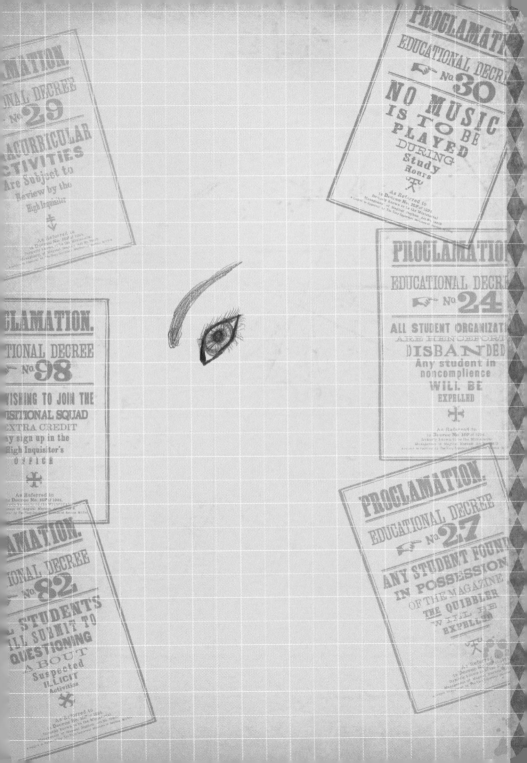

SEEKER

PROCLAMATION.
EDUCATIONAL DECREE
No. 30
NO MUSIC
IS TO BE
PLAYED
DURING
Study
Hours

PROCLAMATION.
NAL DECREE
No. 29
ACURRICULAR
CTIVITIES
Are Subject to
Review by the
High Inquisitor

PROCLAMATION.
EDUCATIONAL DECREE
No. 24
ALL STUDENT ORGANIZATI
ARE HENCEFORTH
DISBANDED
Any student in
noncompliance
WILL BE
EXPELLED

CLAMATION.
TIONAL DECREE
No. 98
ISHING TO JOIN THE
SITIONAL SQUAD
EXTRA CREDIT
y sign up in the
High Inquisitor's
OFFICE

PROCLAMATION.
EDUCATIONAL DECREE
No. 27
ANY STUDENT FOUND
IN POSSESSION
OF THE MAGAZINE
THE QUIBBLER
WILL BE
EXPELLED

AMATION.
IONAL DECREE
No. 82
STUDENTS
LL SUBMIT TO
QUESTIONING
ABOUT
Suspected
ILLICIT
Activities

GRYFFINDOR

Let's All Just Keep Our Fingers Crossed And Hope for The Best!

_____

_____

_____

_____

_____

_____

_____

_____

_____

_____

_____

_____

_____

_____

SEEKER

GRYFFINDOR

Let's All Just Keep Our Fingers Crossed And Hope for The Best.

SEEKER

GRYFFINDOR

Let's All Just Keep Our Fingers Crossed And Hope for The Best.

_____
_____
_____
_____
_____
_____
_____
_____
_____
_____
_____
_____
_____
_____
_____
_____

SEEKER

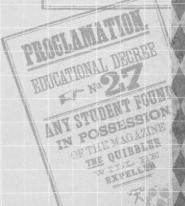

GRYFFINDOR

Let's All Just Keep Our Fingers Crossed And Hope for The Best!

SEEKER

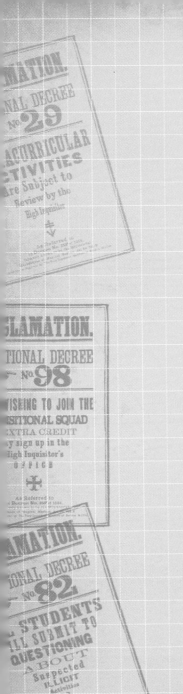

GRYFFINDOR.

Let's All Just Keep Our

Fingers Crossed And Hope for The Best!

_____

_____

_____

_____

_____

_____

_____

_____

_____

_____

_____

_____

_____

_____

_____

_____

SEEKER

GRYFFINDOR

Let's All Just Keep Our
Fingers Crossed And Hope for The Best.

SEEKER

GRYFFINDOR

Let's All Just Keep Our Fingers Crossed And Hope for The Best!

_____

_____

_____

_____

_____

_____

_____

_____

_____

_____

_____

_____

_____

_____

_____

_____

SEEKER

GRYFFINDOR

Let's All Just Keep Our Fingers Crossed And Hope for The Best!

SEEKER

GRYFFINDOR.

Let's All Just Keep Our Fingers Crossed And Hope for The Best!

_____
_____
_____
_____
_____
_____
_____
_____
_____
_____
_____
_____
_____
_____
_____

SEEKER

PROCLAMATION.
EDUCATIONAL DECREE
☞ No. 30
NO MUSIC
IS TO BE
PLAYED
DURING
Study
Hours

PROCLAMATION.
EDUCATIONAL DECREE
☞ No. 24
ALL STUDENT ORGANIZATIONS
ARE HENCEFORTH
DISBANDED
Any student in
noncompliance
WILL BE
EXPELLED

MATION.
NAL DECREE
No. 29
ACURRICULAR
TIVITIES
re Subject to
Review by the
High Inquisitor

LAMATION.
TIONAL DECREE
No. 98
ISHING TO JOIN THE
SITIONAL SQUAD
XTRA CREDIT
y sign up in the
igh Inquisitor's
OFFICE

MATION.
NAL DECREE
No. 82
STUDENTS
LL SUBMIT TO
QUESTIONING
ABOUT
Suspected
ILLICIT
Activities

PROCLAMATION.
EDUCATIONAL DECREE
☞ No. 27
ANY STUDENT FOUND
IN POSSESSION
OF THE MAGAZINE
THE QUIBBLER
WILL BE
EXPELLED

GRYFFINDOR

Let's All Just Keep Our
Fingers Crossed And Hope for The Best.

SEEKER

_____

_____

_____

_____

_____

_____

_____

_____

_____

_____

_____

_____

_____

_____

_____

_____

SEEKER

PROCLAMATION.
EDUCATIONAL DECREE
No. 30
NO MUSIC
IS TO BE
PLAYED
DURING
Study
Hours

PROCLAMATION.
EDUCATIONAL DECREE
No. 24
ALL STUDENT ORGANIZATI
ARE HENCEFORT
DISBANDED
Any student in
noncompliance
WILL BE
EXPELLED

...MATION.
...AL DECREE
No. 29
...ACURRICULAR
...TIVITIES
...re Subject to
Review by the
High Inquisitor

...LAMATION.
...TIONAL DECREE
No. 98
...ISHING TO JOIN THE
...SITIONAL SQUAD
...XTRA CREDIT
...y sign up in the
...igh Inquisitor's
OFFICE

PROCLAMATION.
EDUCATIONAL DECREE
No. 27
ANY STUDENT FOUN
IN POSSESSION
OF THE MAGAZINE
THE QUIBBLER
WILL BE
EXPELLED

...MATION.
...ONAL DECREE
No. 82
...STUDENTS
...LL SUBMIT TO
...QUESTIONING
ABOUT
Suspected
ILLICIT
Activities

GRYFFINDOR

Let's All Just Keep Our

Fingers Crossed And Hope for The Best!

_____

_____

_____

_____

_____

_____

_____

_____

_____

_____

_____

_____

_____

_____

_____

_____

_____

SEEKER

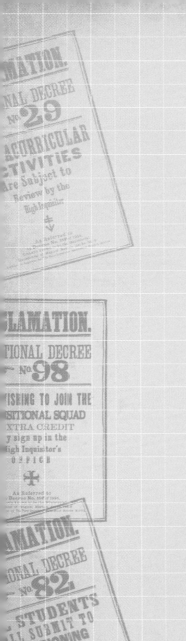

SEEKER

PROCLAMATION.
EDUCATIONAL DECREE
No. 30
NO MUSIC
IS TO BE
PLAYED
DURING
Study
Hours

PROCLAMATION.
EDUCATIONAL DECREE
No. 24
ALL STUDENT ORGANIZATIONS
ARE HENCEFORTH
DISBANDED
Any student in
noncompliance
WILL BE
EXPELLED

PROCLAMATION.
NAL DECREE
No. 29
CURRICULAR
TIVITIES
re Subject to
Review by the
High Inquisitor

LAMATION.
IONAL DECREE
No. 98
ISHING TO JOIN THE
SITIONAL SQUAD
XTRA CREDIT
sign up in the
gh Inquisitor's
OFFICE

MATION.
NAL DECREE
No. 82
STUDENTS
LL SUBMIT TO
UESTIONING
ABOUT
Suspected
ILLICIT
Activities

PROCLAMATION.
EDUCATIONAL DECREE
No. 27
ANY STUDENT FOUND
IN POSSESSION
OF THE MAGAZINE
THE QUIBBLER
WILL BE
EXPELLED

_____

_____

_____

_____

_____

_____

_____

_____

_____

_____

_____

_____

_____

_____

_____

_____

SEEKER

PROCLAMATION.
EDUCATIONAL DECREE
No 30
NO MUSIC IS TO BE PLAYED
DURING
Study
Hours

PROCLAMATION.
EDUCATIONAL DECREE
No 29
EXTRACURRICULAR ACTIVITIES
Are Subject to
Review by the
High Inquisitor

PROCLAMATION.
EDUCATIONAL DECREE
No 24
ALL STUDENT ORGANIZATIONS
ARE HENCEFORTH
DISBANDED
Any student in
noncompliance
WILL BE
EXPELLED

PROCLAMATION.
EDUCATIONAL DECREE
No 98
WISHING TO JOIN THE
INQUISITIONAL SQUAD
FOR EXTRA CREDIT
sign up in the
High Inquisitor's
OFFICE

PROCLAMATION.
EDUCATIONAL DECREE
No 27
ANY STUDENT FOUND
IN POSSESSION
OF THE MAGAZINE
THE QUIBBLER
WILL BE
EXPELLED

PROCLAMATION.
EDUCATIONAL DECREE
No 82
STUDENTS
WILL SUBMIT TO
QUESTIONING
ABOUT
Suspected
ILLICIT
Activities

GRYFFINDOR

Let's All Just Keep Our

Fingers Crossed And Hope for The Best!

_____
_____
_____
_____
_____
_____
_____
_____
_____
_____
_____
_____
_____
_____
_____
_____
_____
_____

SEEKER

SEEKER

SEEKER

GRYFFINDOR

Let's All Just Keep Our

Fingers Crossed And Hope for The Best

_____

_____

_____

_____

_____

_____

_____

_____

_____

_____

_____

_____

_____

_____

_____

_____

SEEKER

GRYFFINDOR.

Let's All Just Keep Our
Fingers Crossed And Hope for The Best!

_____

_____

_____

_____

_____

_____

_____

_____

_____

_____

_____

_____

_____

_____

_____

_____

_____

SEEKER

_____

_____

_____

_____

_____

_____

_____

_____

_____

_____

_____

_____

_____

_____

_____

_____

_____

SEEKER

GRYFFINDOR

Let's All Just Keep Our
Fingers Crossed And Hope for The Best.

SEEKER

PROCLAMATION.
EDUCATIONAL DECREE
No. 29
EXTRACURRICULAR
ACTIVITIES
Are Subject to
Review by the
High Inquisitor

PROCLAMATION.
EDUCATIONAL DECREE
No. 30
NO MUSIC
IS TO BE
PLAYED
DURING
Study
Hours

PROCLAMATION.
EDUCATIONAL DECREE
No. 24
ALL STUDENT ORGANIZATIONS
ARE HENCEFORTH
DISBANDED
Any student in
noncompliance
WILL BE
EXPELLED

PROCLAMATION.
EDUCATIONAL DECREE
No. 98
WISHING TO JOIN THE
INQUISITIONAL SQUAD
FOR EXTRA CREDIT
May sign up in the
High Inquisitor's
OFFICE

PROCLAMATION.
EDUCATIONAL DECREE
No. 82
STUDENTS
WILL SUBMIT TO
QUESTIONING
ABOUT
Suspected
ILLICIT
Activities

PROCLAMATION.
EDUCATIONAL DECREE
No. 27
ANY STUDENT FOUND
IN POSSESSION
OF THE MAGAZINE
THE QUIBBLER
WILL BE
EXPELLED

_____

_____

_____

_____

_____

_____

_____

_____

_____

_____

_____

_____

_____

_____

_____

SEEKER

GRYFFINDOR.

Let's All Just Keep Our Fingers Crossed And Hope for The Best!

SEEKER

GRYFFINDOR.

Let's All Just Keep Our Fingers Crossed And Hope for The Best!

SEEKER

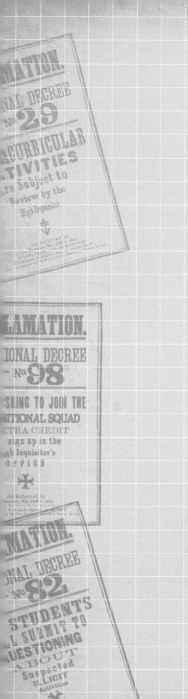

GRYFFINDOR

Let's All Just Keep Our
Fingers Crossed And Hope for The Best

_____

_____

_____

_____

_____

_____

_____

_____

_____

_____

_____

_____

_____

_____

_____

SEEKER

GRYFFINDOR

Let's All Just Keep Our Fingers Crossed And Hope for The Best!

_____

_____

_____

_____

_____

_____

_____

_____

_____

_____

_____

_____

_____

_____

_____

_____

_____

SEEKER

GRYFFINDOR

Let's All Just Keep Our Fingers Crossed And Hope for The Best!

SEEKER

_____

_____

_____

_____

_____

_____

_____

_____

_____

_____

_____

_____

_____

_____

_____

SEEKER

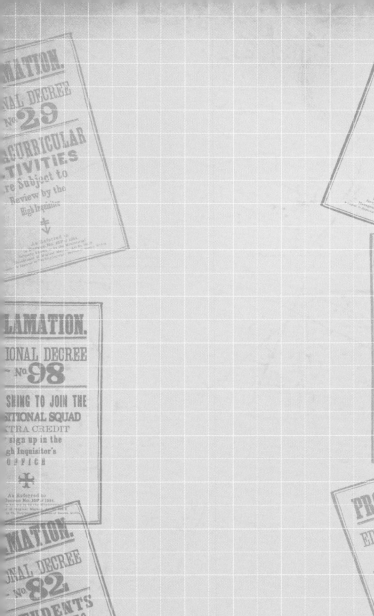
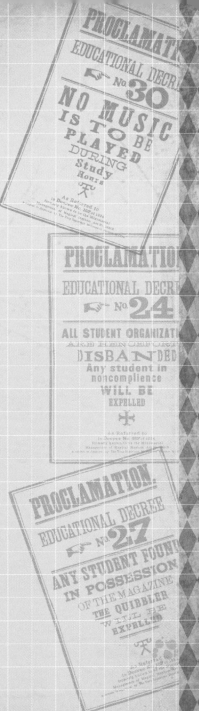

GRYFFINDOR

Let's All Just Keep Our
Fingers Crossed And Hope for The Best.

GRYFFINDOR

Let's All Just Keep Our Fingers Crossed And Hope for The Best

SEEKER

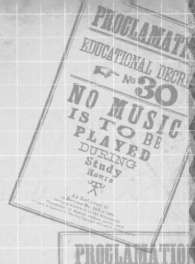

GRYFFINDOR

Let's All Just Keep Our
Fingers Crossed And Hope for The Best!

_____

_____

_____

_____

_____

_____

_____

_____

_____

_____

_____

_____

_____

_____

_____

_____

_____

SEEKER

GRYFFINDOR

Let's All Just Keep Our Fingers Crossed And Hope for The Best!